SECURE TRANSPORT

Can you ensure the convoy of prisoners travel securely from the station in the mountains to LEGO CITY? Draw the route without taking your pencil off the page. Don't touch the edge! It would mean falling off the cliff!

KT-116-629

START

THE FASTEST ACADEMY CADET COMPLETED THE TASK IN TWENTY SECONDS. CAN YOU DO IT FASTER?

FINISH

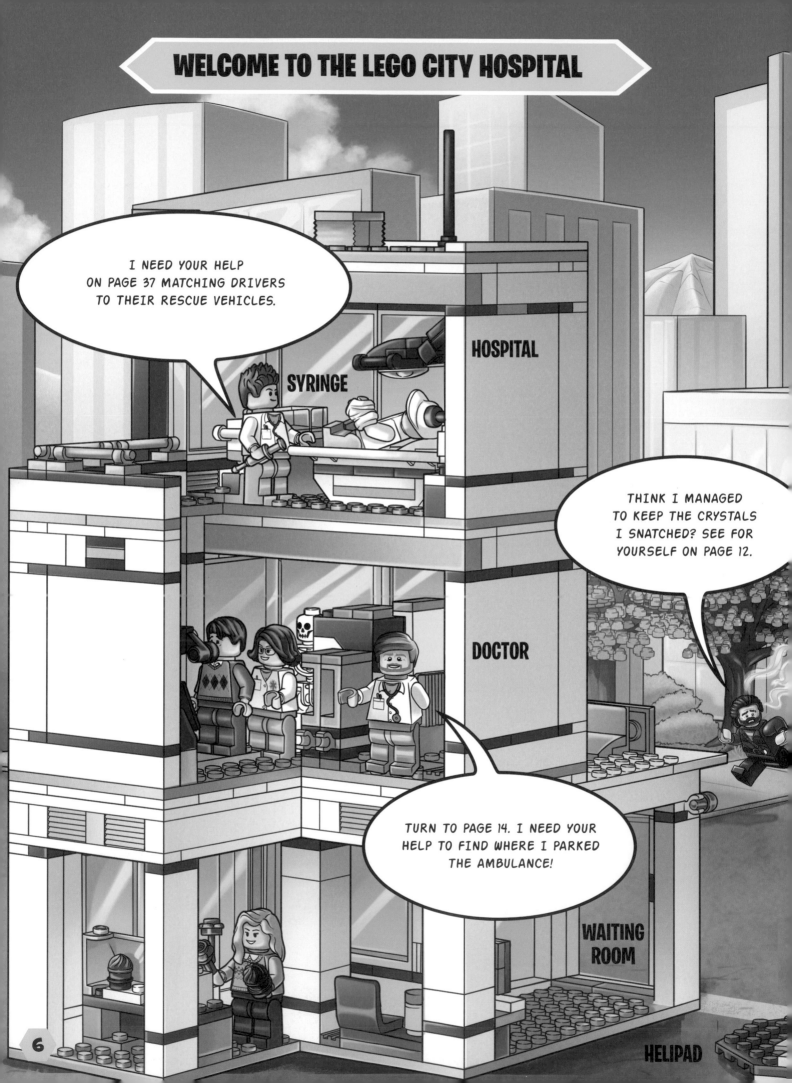

LEGO® ANNUAL 2020

CONTENTS

HOW TO BUILD EMMET

BREAKING NEWS!

WE'D LIKE TO INVITE YOU TO OUR SPECIAL LIVE REPORT STRAIGHT FROM THE LEGO® CITY COFFEE BAR!

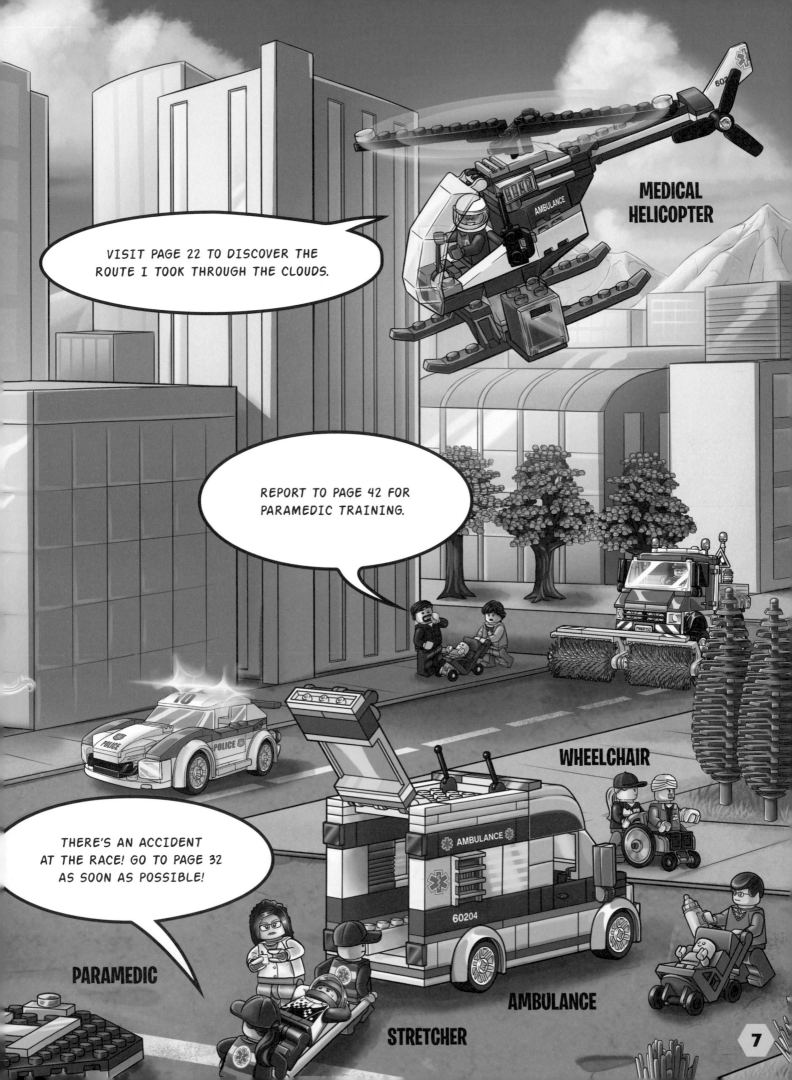

THERE'S ONLY ONE EMMET

One of the pictures of Emmet is different from the rest.
Can you spot it?

HEART ATTACK!

Sweet Mayhem is attacking with exploding hearts!
Can you find 13 of them in the picture?

HERE'S EMMET!

Emmet Brickowski is a completely ordinary, inconspicuous guy.

GOOD MORNING, EVERYBODY!

Once, Emmet was considered to be The Special.

But it turned out that he had actually been chosen to be The Special by accident.

THE PROPHECY, FIGHTS, PURSUITS - THEY WERE ALL A GREAT ADVENTURE! AND LOTS OF STUFF HAPPENED!

YOU DIDN'T NEED TO ADD THAT PART!

Emmet is known for his good mood.

TWO COFFEES PLEASE, ONE BLACK, ONE WITH JUST A TOUCH OF CREAM AND 25 SUGARS. GOTTA MAKE THE MOST OF IT WHILE THE CAFÉ'S STILL STANDING!

His level-headed friend Lucy needs to bring him down to earth sometimes.

Although he's an ordinary guy, he's capable of extraordinary things.

Emmet is very serious about friendship. That's why he thinks that he only has one special friend.

But he has a lot more friends!

SMELLY EMERGENCY

Take a look at the set of pictures and connect them into a story by writing in numbers from 1 to 4.

Look at the pictures again to find all the crystals the robber lost during his stinky adventure.

GET OUT OF THE WAY!

Lead the ambulance carrying the hurt biker so that it reaches the hospital as fast as possible. Avoid the streets with red lights.

FINISH

START

AMBULANCE

60204

ON DUTY

What is the parking space number of the ambulance that will be answering emergency calls today? Read the doctor's hints to find out.

___ ___ ___ ___ ___
A   B   C   D   E

A. 5+1= ?
B. The number of fingers on one hand.
C. The number of ears you have.
D. The number of days in a week.
E. The number of paws a dog has.

SIREN ON!

Lead the ambulance to the patient in need using the information provided by the dispatcher.

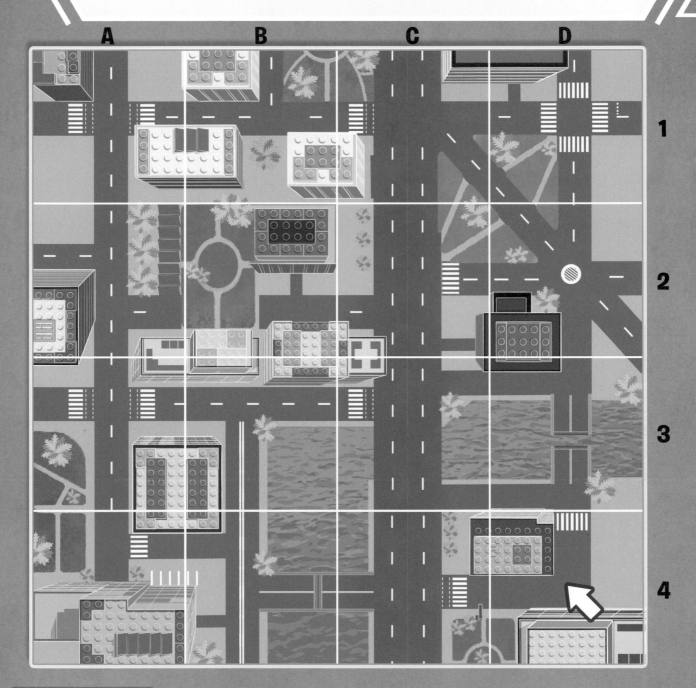

ON YOUR WAY AVOID:

B2

The patient is waiting in the house built from grey and red bricks.

C3

Traffic jam.

D3

Open drawbridge.

A4

Roadworks.

WHOSE X-RAY IS THIS?

The doctor is ready to put a cast on his patient.
But whose x-ray is he looking for?

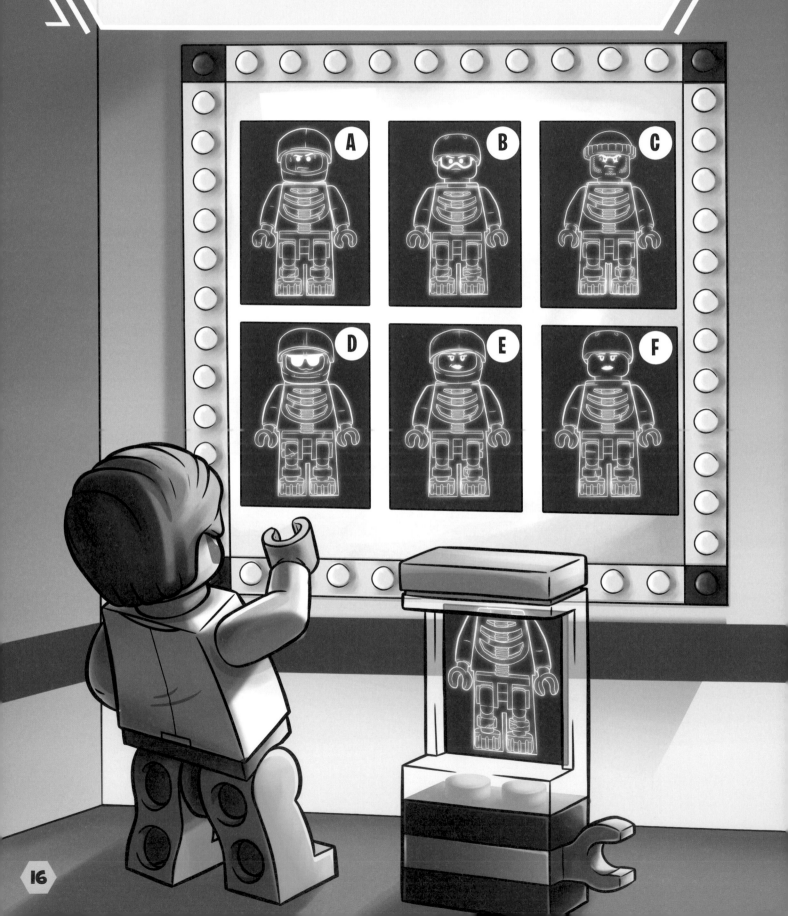

WHO IS MISSING?

Take a look at the four rows of characters. Each row is missing one person. Find out who they are and assign the right letter to each missing person. Each character can appear only once in a row.

1

2

3

4

A   B   C   D

ODD ONE OUT

In each of the four photos below there is someone who doesn't quite belong! Can you spot the odd one out each time? The symbols in the boxes give you a hint about which character doesn't fit into the group.

FISHED OUT

As part of practising new crook-catching techniques, the mountain officers have tested an enormous net. Think you could do it too? Number the pictures from the action in the correct order.

HELICOPTER IN ACTION

Which route through the clouds did the helicopter take?
Circle the hole it made.

THE FORECAST
WAS CLOUDY, BUT IT'S LOOKING
PRETTY CLEAR TO ME!

SUSPECT STAKEOUT

In a moment, Chase McCain will test how well you can spot suspects in a stakeout. Take a look at the mugshots Chase is holding and circle the two leaders of the gang in the picture. Can you also find and circle five red crowbars?

5 x

LOW SUPPLIES

Which item should the doctor place in each space marked with a question mark to complete the pattern? Each piece of medical equipment can only appear once in each row or column.

I THINK WE SHOULD DISCUSS THIS AT A STAFF MEETING!

TO THE RESCUE!

The three characters need your help! Using information from the speech bubbles, lead them to the right places by writing the appropriate letters inside the circles.

Are there more skiers or snowboarders in the picture? Tick the correct symbol.

SIGN UP HERE TO JOIN THE SNOWBOARDING COMPETITION!

A NEW RIDE

Behold ... a new ambulance for emergency workers. It isn't very visible right now, so connect the dots and colour it in. Then we'll set out on a mission with it!

EMERGENCY GEAR

Help the paramedic gather his equipment – he'll only need five items! Let's get to it!

RAPID RACE RESPONSE

There's been an accident at the annual LEGO CITY races!
Thankfully, the paramedics and the doctor are already on
the scene. Find all the drivers that were involved.

There are many tools scattered in the picture.
Count them all and write their number in the box.

33

PHOTO FINISH

The same picture from a rescue mission appeared in these two newspapers. It's astonishing that there are ten differences between them! Can you spot the differences?

Find the fragments in the illustration above.

STANDOUT SUIT

Emergency workers need uniforms that help them stand out from the crowd. Design a new suit for this rescue helicopter pilot.

TEAM OF HEROES

This emergency requires the assistance of a police officer, a doctor and a firefighter. Lead the drivers to their vehicles by connecting the bricks with their machines.

COSMIC DIFFERENCES

Rex is a cosmic adventurer and raptor trainer!
Spot eight differences between these two photos of him.

THE CAMERA LOVES ME.

THEY ARE SOOO CUTE!

Emmet is looking for Lucy and the rest of his kidnapped friends, together with Rex – raptor trainer, space cowboy and well-known adventurer. Their search has led them to a mysterious planet, somewhere in the Systar System ...

PRACTICE MAKES PERFECT

What is going on during the paramedic training?
Can you find ten unusual situations in this picture?

Find out how many syringes there
are on the page: 6, 7 or 8?

43

NAVIGATION SKILLS

You'll start your training with the constable who will show you how to cross mountain bridges. First activity: draw in the missing bridges.

START

DOUGHNUTS IN DANGER

The LEGO CITY police nailed some crooks at the station. Those rascals wanted to steal the entire doughnut supply from the police storeroom! Can you circle the ten differences between the pictures showing the crime?

Test your skills! Help the policemen locate all the robbers rummaging through the storeroom! Write their number in the box.

47

LATE FOR THE PARTY

Use the elements from the box below to patch up the road for the girl, so that she can get to the party on time.

A   B   C   D   E

Catch the bunch of balloons that has one of each colour. Find and circle it!

49

QUICK THINKING

Crooks disguised as clowns have just robbed the bank! They've thrown four different brick combinations in the air to slow down the officers. Find and count the different brick combinations, before all the bricks tumble!

EQUIPMENT INSPECTION

Time for an equipment inspection! Compare a city policeman with a mountain policeman and match all the common elements in their equipment.

UNDERCOVER TRAINING

The first lesson in undercover work is blending in.
Get Chase McCain ready for each assignment by drawing
the right disguise for the situation.

COLLECTING EVIDENCE

Help the policemen in this securing evidence exercise.
Look at the picture and circle all the objects the arrested crook
has dropped.

MOUNTAIN PATROL

Chase McCain will teach you how to patrol the difficult mountain areas. Let's see how well you handle a patrol at high altitude. Look at the infrared silhouettes to the right and mark the crooks' whereabouts in the area below.

ANSWERS

p. 8

K

p. 9

p. 12

4   1
3   2

p. 13

p. 14

6   4   2   7   4

p. 15

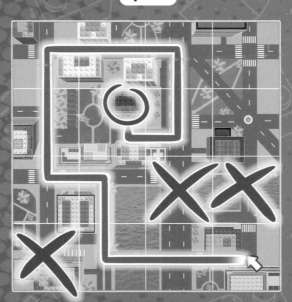

p. 16

B

p. 17

B   A   D   C
1   2   3   4

p. 18–19

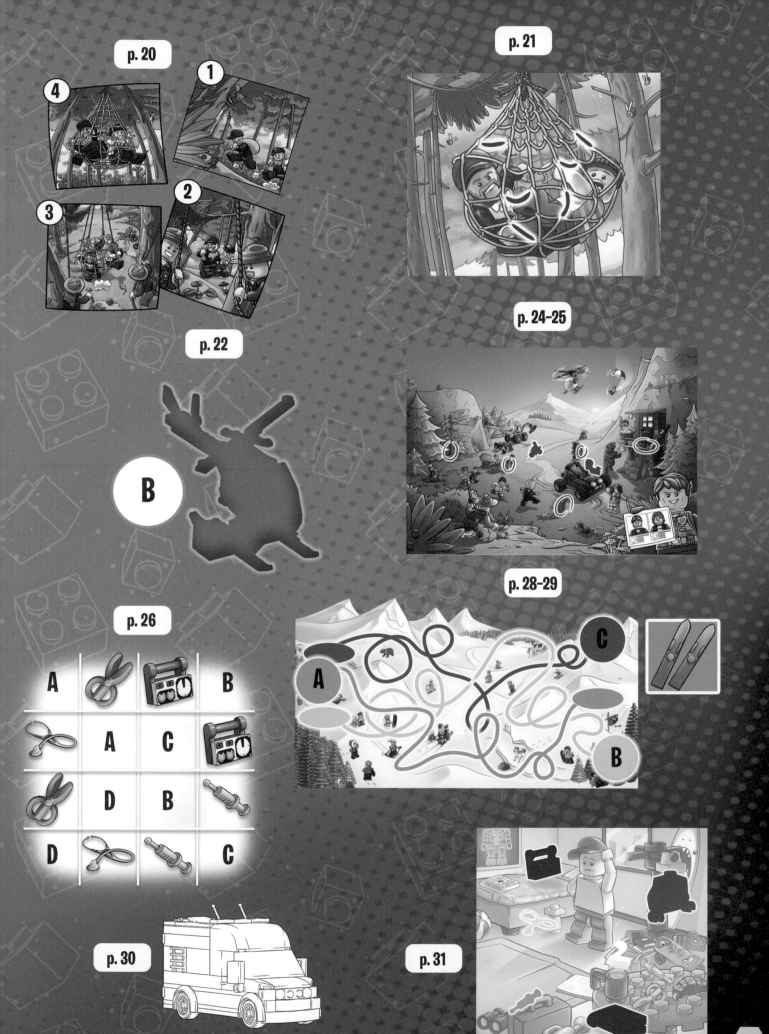

p. 20

4

1

3

2

p. 21

p. 22

B

p. 24-25

p. 26

A | | | B
A	C
D	B
D | | | C

p. 28-29

A

C

B

p. 30

p. 31

ANSWERS

p. 32-33

p. 34-35

p. 37

p. 38-39

p. 42-43

p. 44-45

p. 46–47

p. 48–49

p. 50–51

p. 52

p. 53

p. 55

p. 56–57